The Easy Ke

Big Band Hits
23 classic songs for keyboard

April In Paris 2

Avalon 4

Begin The Beguine 6

Come Fly With Me 8

Fly Me To The Moon 10

Get Happy 12

Indian Summer 14

In The Mood 16

It Had To Be You 18

It's Only A Paper Moon 20

La Vie En Rose 22

My Heart Stood Still 24

Night And Day 26

Oh, Lady Be Good! 28

On The Sunny Side Of The Street 30

Secret Love 32

September Song 34

A String Of Pearls 36

Tea For Two 38

Thou Swell 40

Tuxedo Junction 42

The Very Thought Of You 44

What Is This Thing Called Love? 46

© International Music Publications Ltd
First published in 1994 by International Music Publications Ltd
International Music Publications Ltd is a Faber Music company
Bloomsbury House 74–77 Great Russell Street London WC1B 3DA
Cover Image Michael Ochs Archive / Redferns Music Picture Library
Music arranged & processed by Barnes Music Engraving Ltd
Printed in England by Caligraving Ltd
All rights reserved

ISBN10: 0-571-52915-1
EAN13: 978-0-571-52915-5

April In Paris

Words by E.Y. Harburg / Music by Vernon Duke

Suggested Registration: Vibraphone
Rhythm: Slow Swing
Tempo: ♩ = 72

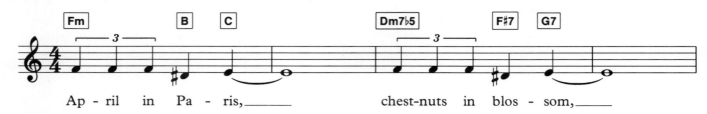

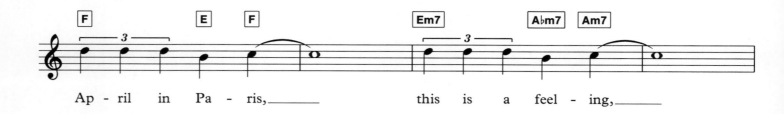

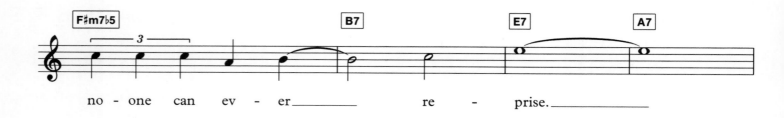

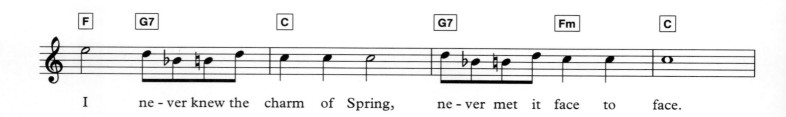

3

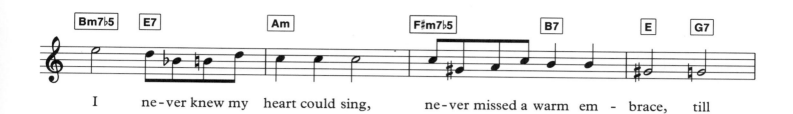

I ne-ver knew my heart could sing, ne-ver missed a warm em - brace, till

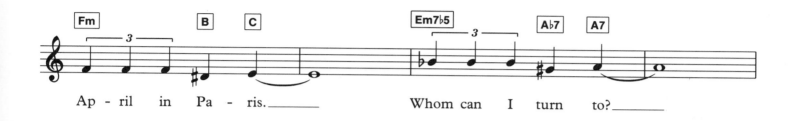

Ap - ril in Pa - ris._____ Whom can I turn to?_____

What have I done to_____ my heart?_____

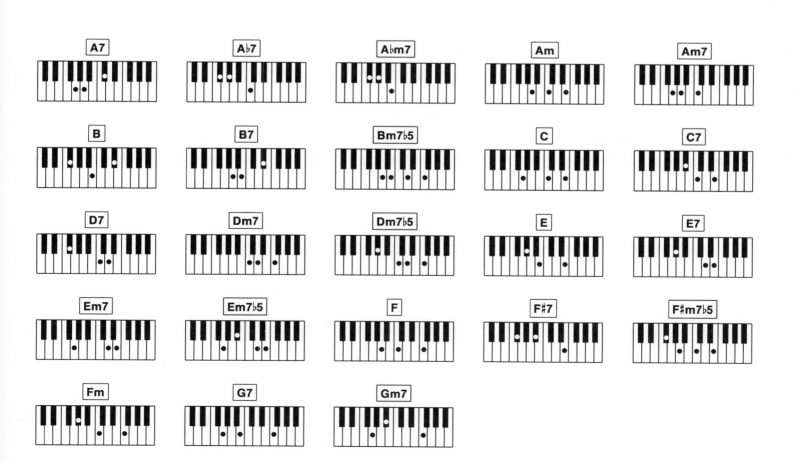

AVALON

Words by Al Jolson and B.G. DeSylva / Music by Vincent Rose

Suggested Registration: Jazz Guitar
Rhythm: Fast Swing
Tempo: ♩ = 200

I found my love in A - va - lon,_____ be -

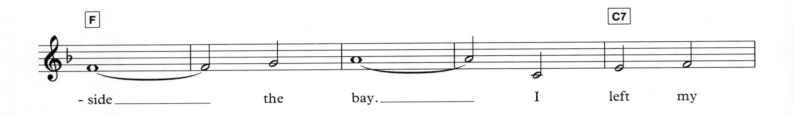

- side _____ the bay. _____ I left my

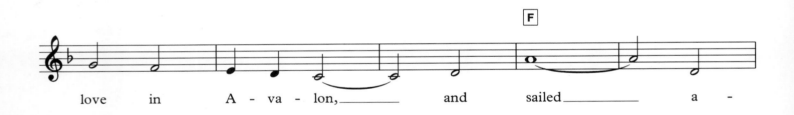

love in A - va - lon, _____ and sailed _____ a -

- way. _____ I dream of her and A - va - lon, _____ from

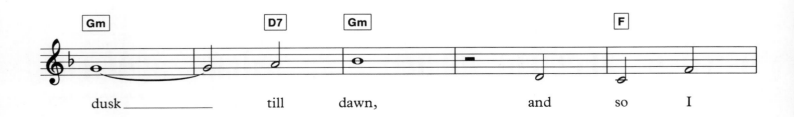

dusk _____ till dawn, and so I

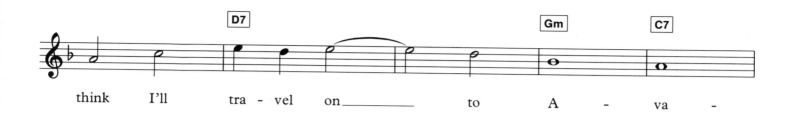

think   I'll   tra - vel   on_____   to   A   -   va -

- lon,_____   and   so   I   think   I'll   tra - vel   on_____   to

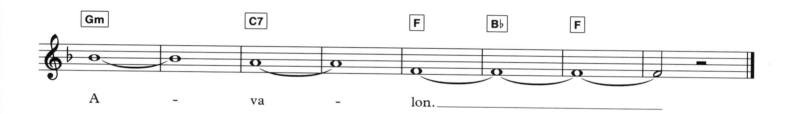

A   -   va   -   lon._____

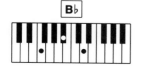
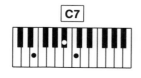
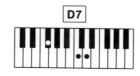
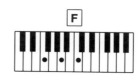
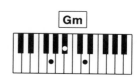

BEGIN THE BEGUINE

Words & Music by Cole Porter

Suggested Registration: Jazz Guitar
Rhythm: Beguine / Latin
Tempo: ♩ = 142

When they be - gin the Be - guine, it

brings back the sound of mu - sic so ten - der, it

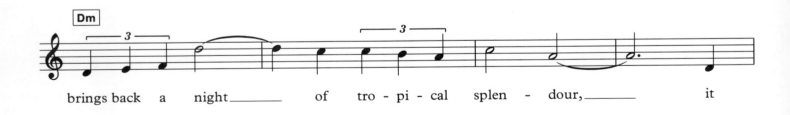

brings back a night of tro - pi - cal splen - dour, it

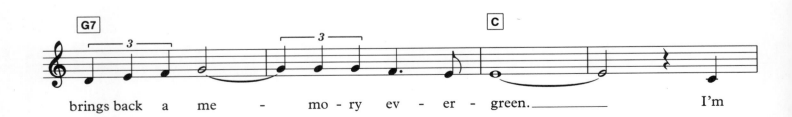

brings back a me - mo - ry ev - er - green. I'm

Warner Chappell Music Ltd., London W1Y 3FA

with you once more_____ un - der the stars,_____ and

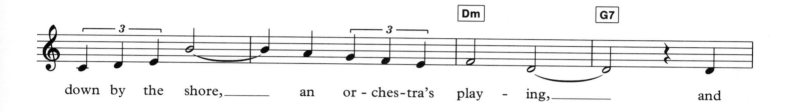

down by the shore,_____ an or - ches-tra's play - ing,_____ and

e - ven the palms_____ seem to be sway - ing,_____

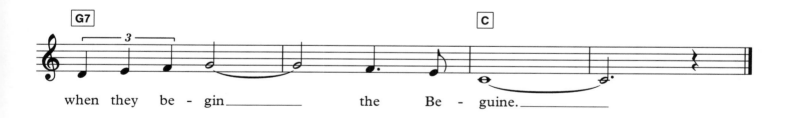

when they be - gin_____ the Be - guine._____

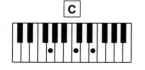

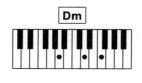

Come Fly With Me

Words by Sammy Cahn / Music by James Van Heusen

Suggested Registration: Vibraphone
Rhythm: Swing
Tempo: ♩ = 128

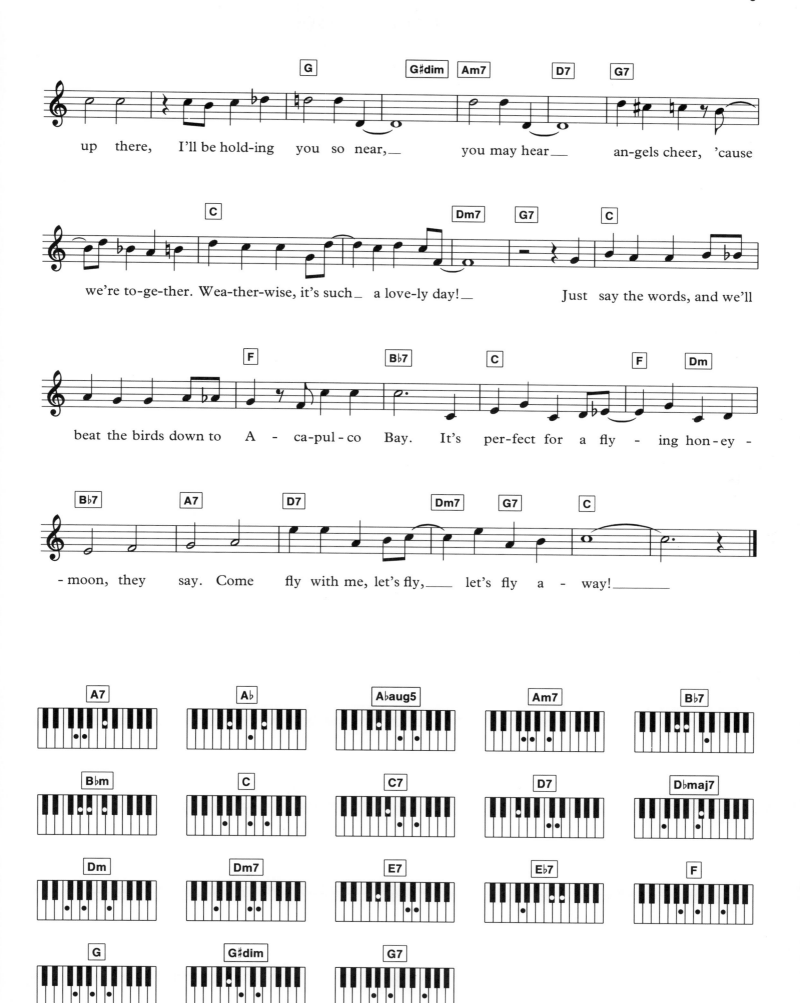

Fly Me To The Moon

Words & Music by Bart Howard

Suggested Registration: Vibraphone
Rhythm: Swing
Tempo: ♩ = 116

Fly me to the moon,__ and let me play a-mong the stars,__

let me see what Spring__ is like on Ju - pi - ter and Mars.__ In

oth - er words, hold my hand,___ in

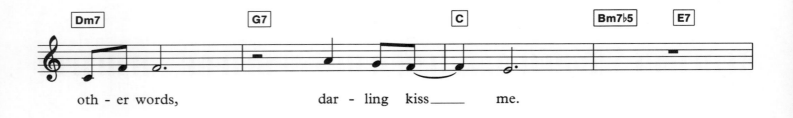

oth - er words, dar - ling kiss___ me.

Fill my heart with song,__ and let me sing for ev - er - more,__

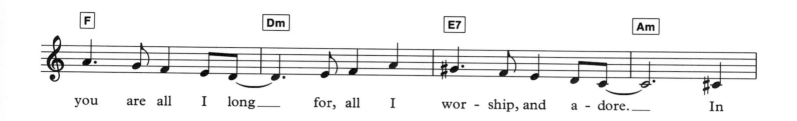

you are all I long___ for, all I wor - ship, and a - dore.___ In

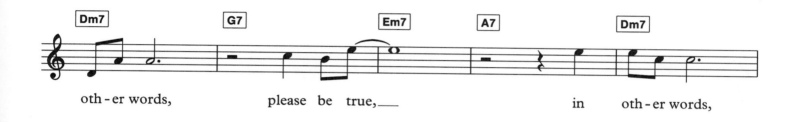

oth - er words, please be true,___ in oth - er words,

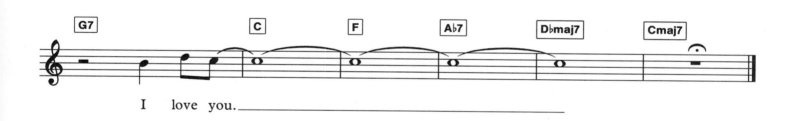

I love you.___

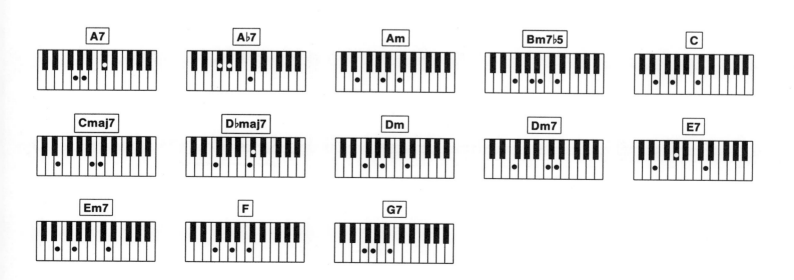

GET HAPPY

Words & Music by Harold Arlen and Ted Koehler

Suggested Registration: Vibraphone
Rhythm: Swing
Tempo: ♩ = 116

Indian Summer

Words by Al Dubin / Music by Victor Herbert

Suggested Registration: Vibraphone
Rhythm: Slow Swing
Tempo: ♩ = 76

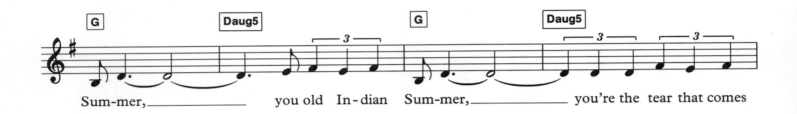

Sum-mer,_____ you old In-dian Sum-mer,_____ you're the tear that comes

af - ter_____ June-time's_ laugh-ter._____ You see so ma-ny

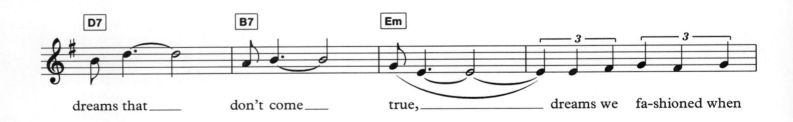

dreams that____ don't come____ true,_____ dreams we fa-shioned when

Sum-mer - time was____ new._____ You are here to watch

Warner Chappell Music Ltd., London W1Y 3FA

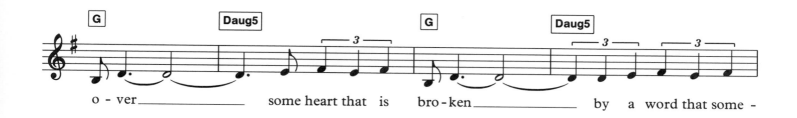

o - ver_____ some heart that is bro - ken_____ by a word that some -

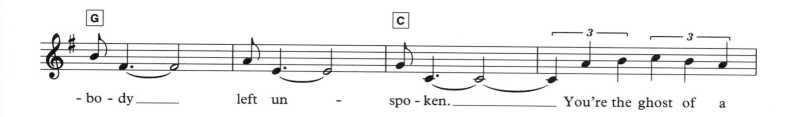

- bo - dy_____ left un - spo - ken._____ You're the ghost of a

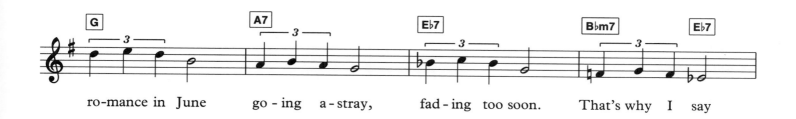

ro - mance in June go - ing a - stray, fad - ing too soon. That's why I say

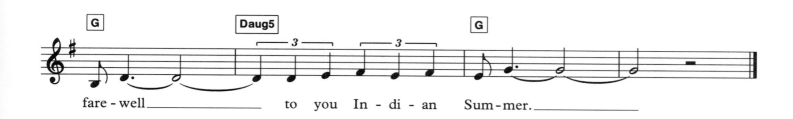

fare - well_____ to you In - di - an Sum - mer._____

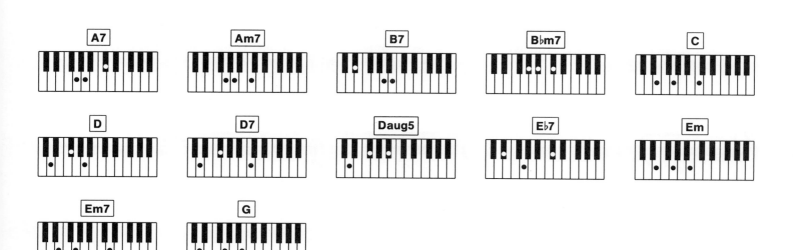

In The Mood

Words & Music by Joe Garland

Suggested Registration: Tenor Saxophone
Rhythm: Swing
Tempo: ♩ = 120

Who's the liv-in' dol-ly with the beau-ti-ful eyes? What a pair o' lips, I'd like to

try 'em for size.＿ I'll just tell her, 'Ba-by, won't you swing it with me?'

Hope she tells me may-be, what a wing it will be.＿ So I said pol-ite-ly, 'Dar-lin',

may I in-trude?' She said, 'Don't keep me wait-ing when I'm in the mood.'

First I held her light-ly, and we start-ed to dance, then I held her tight-ly, what a

drea-my ro-mance, and I said, 'Hey ba-by, it's a quar-ter to three,

17

It Had To Be You

Words by Gus Kahn / Music by Isham Jones

Suggested Registration: Jazz Guitar
Rhythm: Medium Swing
Tempo: ♩ = 120

It had to be you,_____ it had to be you,_____

__ I wan-dered a - round,_ and fi-nal-ly found_ the some-bo-dy who_____

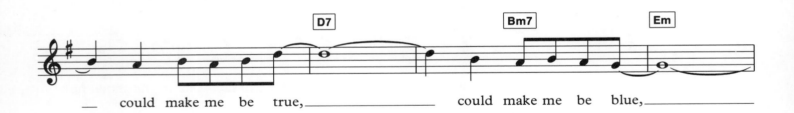

__ could make me be true,_____ could make me be blue,_____

__ and e - ven be glad_ just to be sad,__ think-ing of you._____

__ Some oth-ers I've seen,_____ might ne-ver be mean,_____

— might ne-ver be cross,— or try to be boss,— but they would-n't do,—

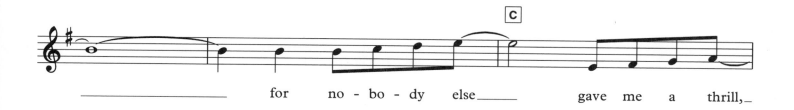

———————— for no - bo - dy else——— gave me a thrill,—

— with all your faults— I love you still.— It had to be you,—

— won-der-ful you,— had to be you.———————

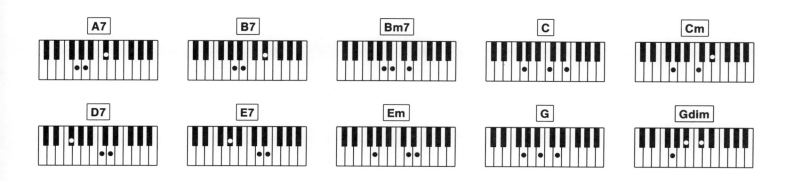

It's Only a Paper Moon

Words by Billy Rose and E.Y. Harburg / Music by Harold Arlen

Suggested Registration: Jazz Guitar
Rhythm: Swing
Tempo: ♩ = 128

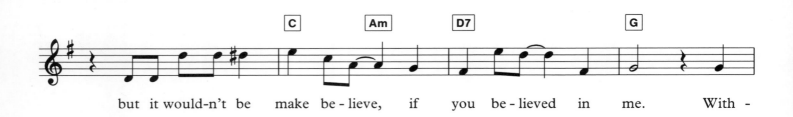

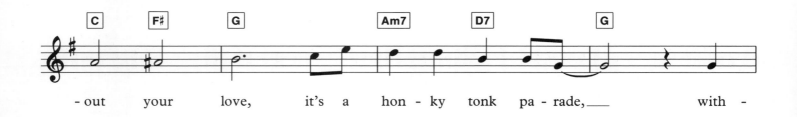

- out your love, it's a me - lo - dy played in a pen - ny ar - cade.

It's a Bar-num and Bai - ley world, just as pho-ney as it can be,__

but it would-n't be make be - lieve, if you be - lieved in me.

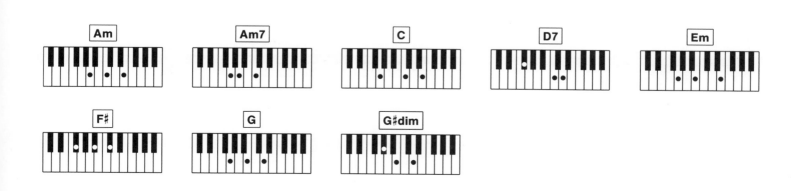

LA VIE EN ROSE

Original French Lyric by Edith Piaf / English Words by Mack David / Music by Louiguy

Suggested Registration: Vibraphone
Rhythm: Slow Swing
Tempo: ♩ = 112

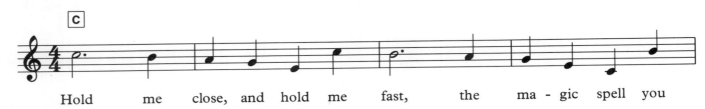

Hold me close, and hold me fast, the ma - gic spell you

cast, this is la vie en rose._____

When you kiss me hea - ven sighs, and though I close my

eyes, I see la vie en rose._____

When you press me to your heart, I'm in a world a -

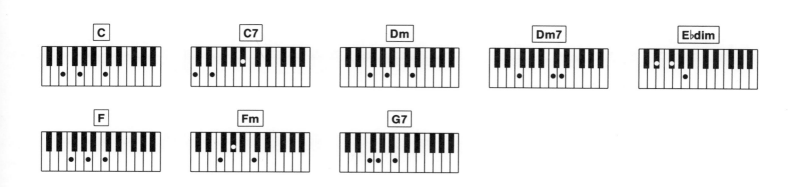

My Heart Stood Still

Words by Lorenz Hart / Music by Richard Rodgers

Suggested Registration: Vibraphone
Rhythm: Slow Jazz Ballad
Tempo: ♩ = 84

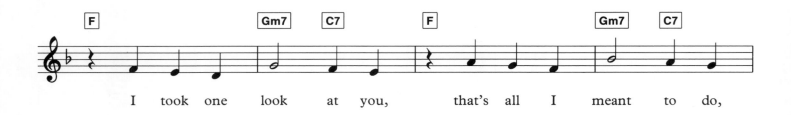

I took one look at you, that's all I meant to do,

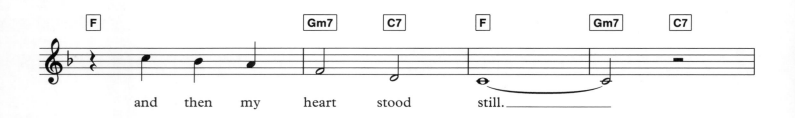

and then my heart stood still._____

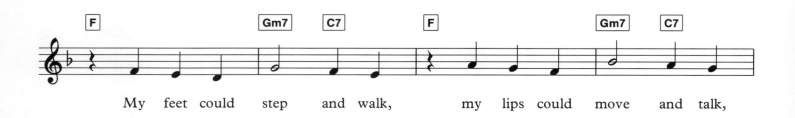

My feet could step and walk, my lips could move and talk,

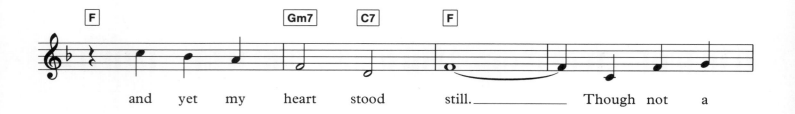

and yet my heart stood still._____ Though not a

sin - gle word was spo - ken, I could tell you knew,＿ that un - felt

clasp of hands,＿ told me so well you knew.＿

I ne - ver lived at all, un - til the thrill of that

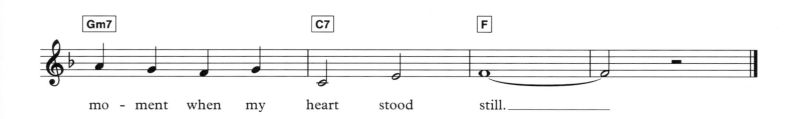

mo - ment when my heart stood still.＿＿＿＿＿

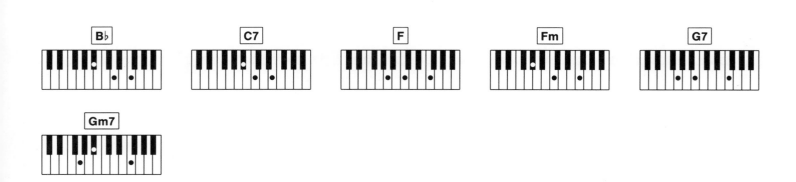

NIGHT AND DAY

Words & Music by Cole Porter

Suggested Registration: Vibraphone
Rhythm: Medium Swing
Tempo: ♩ = 96

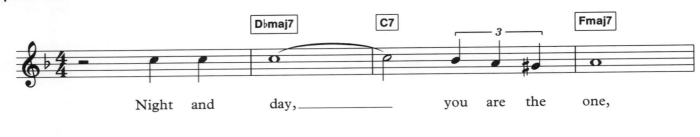

Night and day, _____ you are the one,

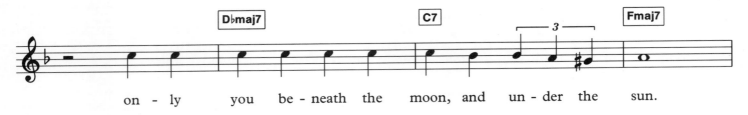

on - ly you be - neath the moon, and un - der the sun.

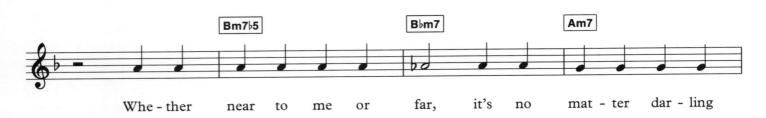

Whe - ther near to me or far, it's no mat - ter dar - ling

where you are, ___ I think of you, ___ night and day. _____

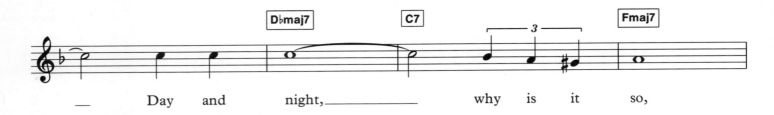

___ Day and night, _____ why is it so,

that this long - ing for you fol - lows wher - ev - er I go?

Oh, Lady Be Good!

Words & Music by George Gershwin and Ira Gershwin

Suggested Registration: Jazz Guitar
Rhythm: Swing
Tempo: ♩ = 140

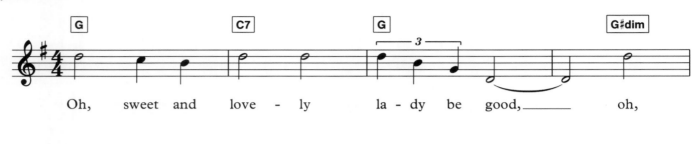

Oh, sweet and love - ly la - dy be good,_____ oh,

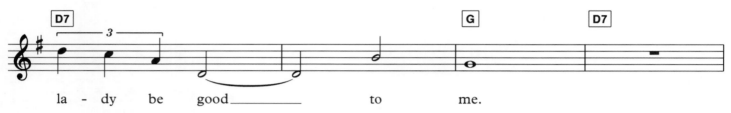

la - dy be good_____ to me.

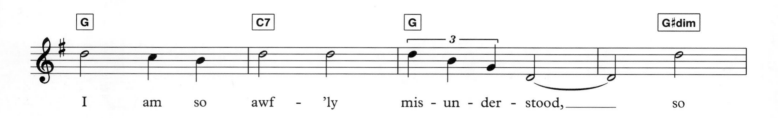

I am so awf - 'ly mis - un - der - stood,_____ so

la - dy be good_____ to me.

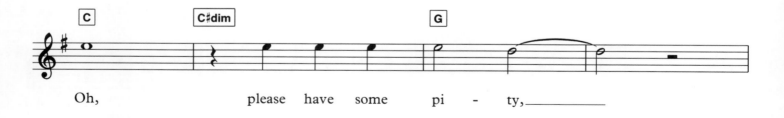

Oh, please have some pi - ty,_____

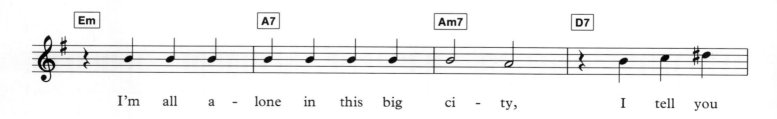

I'm all a - lone in this big ci - ty, I tell you

On The Sunny Side Of The Street

Words by Dorothy Fields / Music by Jimmy McHugh

Suggested Registration: Vibraphone
Rhythm: Fast Swing
Tempo: ♩ = 144

Grab your

coat, and get your hat,   leave your wor - ry on the door - step,

just di - rect your feet   to the sun - ny side— of the street.   Can't you

hear a pit - ter - pat,   and that hap - py tune is your step?

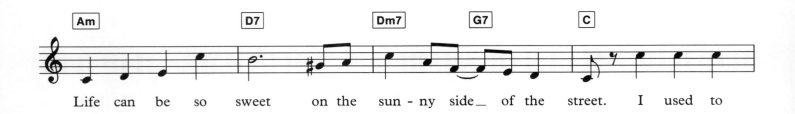

Life can be so sweet   on the sun - ny side— of the street.   I used to

Secret Love

Words by Paul Francis Webster / Music by Sammy Fain

Suggested Registration: Vibraphone
Rhythm: Slow Jazz Ballad
Tempo: ♩ = 94

Once I had a se - cret love, that lived with -

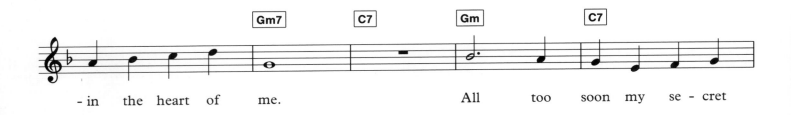

- in the heart of me. All too soon my se - cret

love, be - came im - pa - tient to be free.

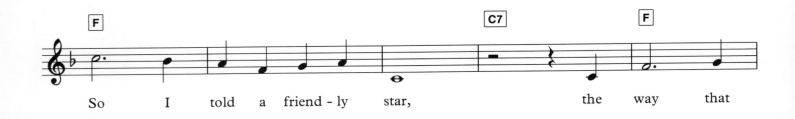

So I told a friend - ly star, the way that

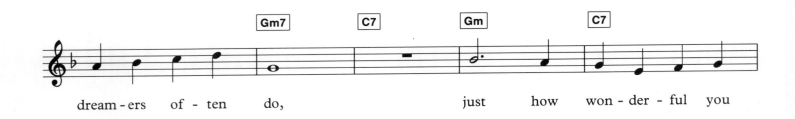

dream - ers of - ten do, just how won - der - ful you

33

34

September Song

Words by Maxwell Anderson / Music by Kurt Weill

Suggested Registration: Jazz Guitar
Rhythm: Swing
Tempo: ♩ = 94

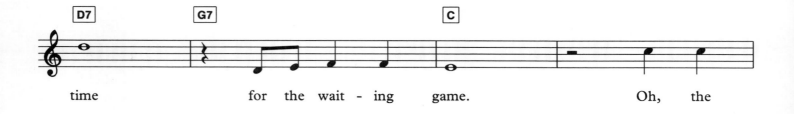

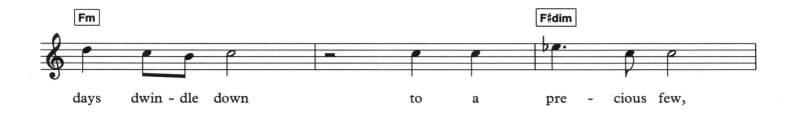

days dwin - dle down   to   a   pre - cious few,

Sep - tem - ber,   No - vem - ber,

and these few pre - cious days   I'll spend with   you,

these pre - cious days   I'll   spend with   you._____

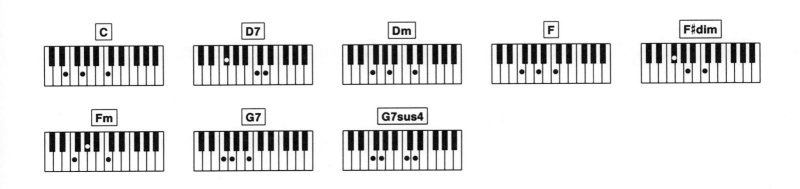

A String Of Pearls

Words by Eddie DeLange / Music by Jerry Gray

Suggested Registration: Tenor Saxophone
Rhythm: Swing
Tempo: ♩ = 116

Ba - by,__ here's__ a five and dime, ba - by,__ now's__ a - bout the time

for a__ string__ of pearls à la Wool - worth.

Ev - ery__ pearl's__ a star a-bove wrapped in__ dreams,__ and filled with love

that old__ string__ of pearls à la Wool - worth.

Till that__ hap - py day in Spring when I__ buy__ the wed-ding ring,

please a__ string__ of pearls à la Wool - worth.

TEA FOR TWO

Words by Irving Caesar / Music by Vincent Youmans

Suggested Registration: Vibraphone
Rhythm: Slow Swing
Tempo: ♩ = 96

Pic - ture you up - on my knee, just tea for two, and two for tea, just

me for you, and you for me a - lone.

No - bo - dy near us to see us, or hear us, no friends or re - la - tions on

week-end va - ca - tions, we won't have it known dear, that we're on the te - le - phone,

dear.　　Day　will break,　and　you'll　a-wake,　and　start　to bake　a

su - gar cake,　for　me　to take　for　all　the boys　to　see._____

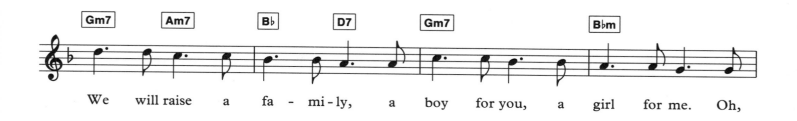

We　will raise　a　fa - mi - ly,　a　boy　for you,　a　girl　for me.　Oh,

can't　you see　how　hap - py　we　would　be?_____

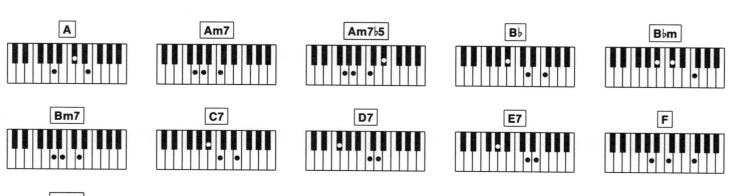

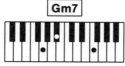

THOU SWELL

Words by Lorenz Hart / Music by Richard Rodgers

Suggested Registration: Vibraphone
Rhythm: Swing
Tempo: ♩ = 84

Thou swell! Thou wit - ty!_____ Thou sweet! Thou

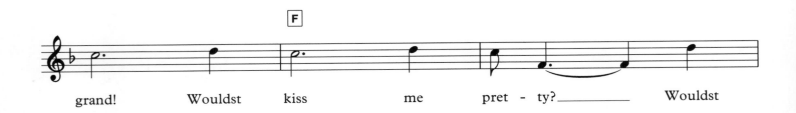

grand! Wouldst kiss me pret - ty?_____ Wouldst

hold my hand? Both thine eyes_____ are cute too;

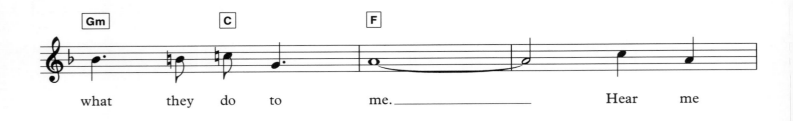

what they do to me._____ Hear me

hol - ler, I choose a sweet lol - la - pa - loo - sa in thee._____ I'd

TUXEDO JUNCTION

Words by Buddy Feyne / Music by Erskine Hawkins, William Johnson and Julian Dash

Suggested Registration: Muted Trumpet
Rhythm: Swing
Tempo: ♩ = 104

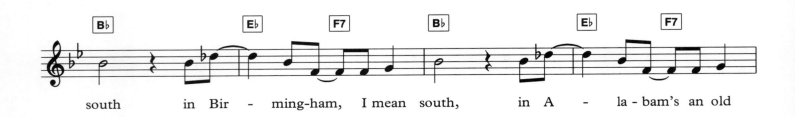

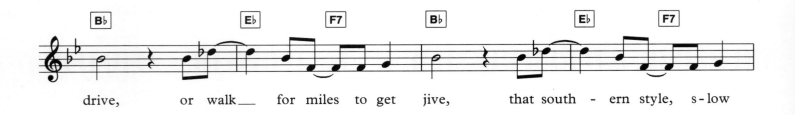

THE VERY THOUGHT OF YOU

Words & Music by Ray Noble

Suggested Registration: *Jazz Guitar*
Rhythm: Slow Swing
Tempo: ♩ = 80

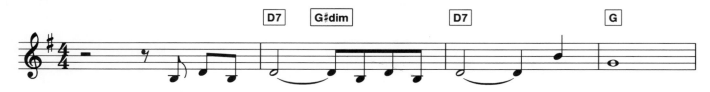

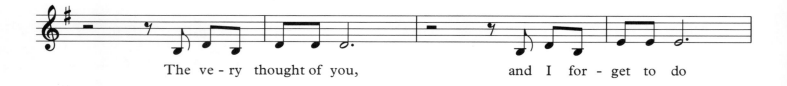

The ve - ry thought of you, and I for - get to do

the lit - tle or - di - na - ry things that ev - ery-one ought to do.

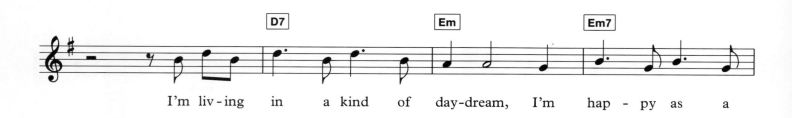

I'm liv - ing in a kind of day-dream, I'm hap - py as a

king, and fool - ish though it may seem, to me_____ that's ev - ery -

- thing. The mere i - dea of you, the long-ing here for you,

you'll ne-ver know how slow the mo - ments go till I'm near to you.

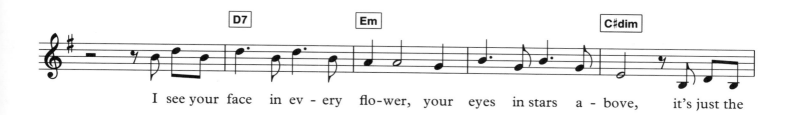

I see your face in ev - ery flo-wer, your eyes in stars a - bove, it's just the

thought of you,___ the ve - ry thought of you, my love._____

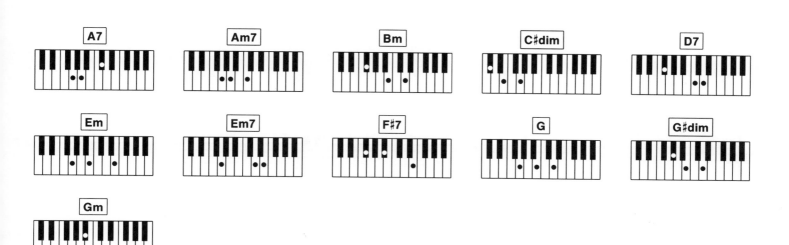

WHAT IS THIS THING CALLED LOVE?

Words & Music by Cole Porter

Suggested Registration: Jazz Guitar
Rhythm: Swing
Tempo: ♩ = 110

What is this thing _____ called love,

this fun - ny thing _____ called love?

Just who can solve _____ its mys - te - ry?

Why should it make _____ a fool of me?

I saw you there _____ one won - der - ful day,

you took my heart,_____ and threw it a - way.

That's why I ask the Lord_____ in hea-ven a - bove,

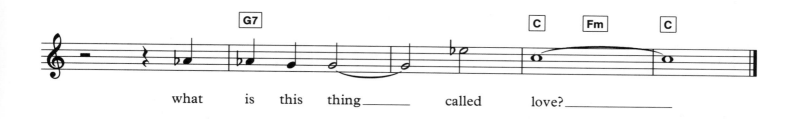

what is this thing_____ called love?_____

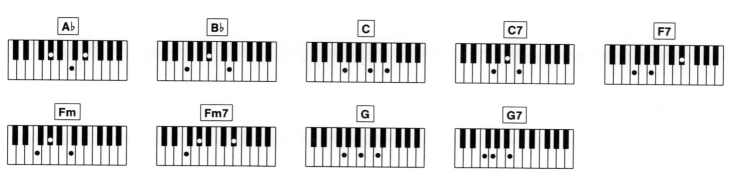

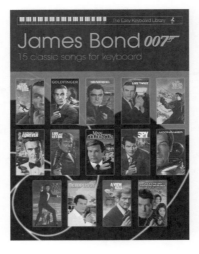